# A
# Pocketful
# of Poems

S C H O L A S T I C
**P**ROFESSIONAL**B**OOKS

NEW YORK • TORONTO • LONDON • AUCKLAND • SYDNEY

# ·····Table of Contents·····

Animals . . . . . . . . . . . . . . . . . . . . . . . . . . . . . . . . . . . 3
Seasons and Special Days . . . . . . . . . . . . . . . . . . . . . 10
Friends and Fun Times . . . . . . . . . . . . . . . . . . . . . . . 16
Haiku . . . . . . . . . . . . . . . . . . . . . . . . . . . . . . . . . . . . 23
Riddles . . . . . . . . . . . . . . . . . . . . . . . . . . . . . . . . . . . 25
Counting Rhymes . . . . . . . . . . . . . . . . . . . . . . . . . . . 28
Take-Away (Subtraction) Rhymes . . . . . . . . . . . . . . . 31

# ········ Introduction ········

Welcome to *A Pocketful of Poems*. The poems in this book have been selected to complement your pocket chart program, and we hope you and your students will enjoy them.

One way to get the most out of these poems is to create your own pocket charts with them, substituting different words for the words in the poem. These poems can also be copied onto chart paper and read aloud as part of guided or shared reading. You might even want to use them as the centerpiece of a thematic bulletin board, or make them into mini-books, or classroom posters you can make and illustrate yourself (or you can invite students to illustrate them!)

However you decide to use these poems, we feel confident that they will help enrich your literature-based reading and writing program. Enjoy!

—The Editors

# The Squirrel

Whisky Frisky,
Hippity hop,
Up he goes
To the tree top!

Whirly, twirly,
Round and round,
Down he scampers
To the ground.

—Unknown

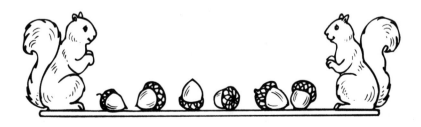

# As I Looked Out

As I looked out on Sunday last,
A fat little pig went hurrying past.
Over his shoulders he wore a shawl,
Although it didn't seem cold at all.
I waved at him, but he didn't see,
For he never so much as looked at me.
Once again, when the moon was high,
I saw the little pig hurrying by;
Back he came at a terrible pace,
The moonlight shone on
        his little pink face,
And he smiled with a
        smile that was
        quite content.
But  I never knew where
        that little pig went.

—Unknown

# Sea Animals

What do you
see in the sea?
Animals moving
free!
Snails and whales
Using their tails.
Seals and eels
Looking for meals.
Catfish, flatfish
Chasing fat fish.
What do see in the sea?
Animals moving free!

—Meish Goldish

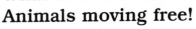

# Baby Animals

Oh, baby, baby, so young and so tame,
Oh, baby, baby, so what is your name?
Baby cow is a calf,
Baby deer is a fawn,
Baby goat is a kid eating
    grass on the lawn.
Baby bear is cub,
Baby hen is a chick,
Baby swan is a cygnet so graceful and quick.
Baby goose is a gosling,
Baby seal is a pup,
Baby cat is a kitten drinking milk from a cup.
Baby sheep is a lamb,
Baby turkey's a poult,
Baby horse is a foal or a filly or colt.
Oh, baby, baby, so young and so tame,
Oh, baby, baby, be proud of your name!

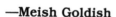

—Meish Goldish

# Animals From A to Z

A is Ape, B is Bee,
C is Clownfish in the sea!

D is Deer, E is Eel,
F's a Fox who wants a meal.

G is Goose, H is Hog,
I's an inchworm on a log.

Jay is J, Koala's K,
L's a Lion far away.

M is Mule, N is Newt,
O's an Ostrich tall and cute.

P is Pig, Q is Quail,
R's a Rat with curly tail.

Snake is S, Turkey's T,
U's the Umbrella bird flying free.

V is Viper, Worm is W,
Bird's X are hatching.
(Does that joke trouble you?)

Yak is Y, Zebra's Z,
Alphabet animals for you and me!

—Meish Goldish

# A Little Squirrel

I saw a little squirrel,
   Sitting in a tree;
He was eating a nut
And wouldn't look at me.

—Child in Winnetka Nursery School

# The Chickens

Said the first little chicken
    With a queer little squirm,
"I wish I could find
    A fat little worm."

Said the next little chicken
    With an odd little shrug,
"I wish I could find
    A fat little slug."

Said the third little chicken
    With a sharp little squeal,
"I wish I could find
    Some nice yellow meal."

Said the fourth little chicken
    With a small sigh of grief,
"I wish I could find
    A little green leaf."

Said the fifth little chicken
    With a faint little moan,
"I wish I could find
    A wee gravel stone."

"Now, see here," said the mother,
    From the green garden patch,
"If you want any breakfast,
    Just come here and scratch."

—Unknown

Animals • • • • • • • • • • • • • • • • • • • • • •    9

# Happy Birthday

Today's the day,
We get to say,
We're happy you were born,
Hooray!

—Helen H. Moore

# Pumpkin, Pumpkin

Pumpkin, pumpkin,
Big and round
Pumpkin, pumpkin,
On the ground.

With my finger
I will trace
A smile upon
Your orange face.

—Jaime A. Lucero

# Thanksgiving

The year has turned its circle,
The seasons come and go.
The harvest is all gathered in
And chilly north winds blow.

Orchards have shared their
        treasures,
The fields, their yellow grain,
So open wide the doorway—
Thanksgiving comes again!

—Unknown

# The Leaves

The leaves had a wonderful frolic,
    They danced to the wind's loud song,
They whirled, and they floated, and scampered,
    They circled and flew along.

The moon saw the little leaves dancing,
    Each looked like a small brown bird.
The man in the moon smiled and listened,
    And this is the song he heard.

The North Wind is calling, is calling,
    And we must whirl round and round,
And then when our dancing is ended
    We'll make a warm quilt for the ground.

—Unknown

# Down
# the Hill

Down, down the hill
How fast I go,
Over the grasses
Under the snow.

The wind must feel
Me going fast.
It whistles as
I'm going past.

Down, down the hill,
My sled and I,
Ever so fast
We fly! We fly!

—Unknown

# Never Mind, March

Never mind, March, we know
When you blow
You're not really mad
Or angry or bad;
You're only blowing the winter away
To get the world ready for April and May.

—Unknown

# The Whirl and Twirl

Like a leaf or a feather,
In the windy, windy weather;
We will whirl around,
And twirl around
And all sink down together.

—Unknown

## Do You Love Me?

Do you love me
Or do you not?
You told me once
But I forgot.

—Unknown

# Mail Carrier

See the mail carrier, swinging along
   Her bag is deep and wide,
And messages from all the world
   Are bundled up inside.

Now she's walking up our street.
   Soon she'll ring my bell.
Perhaps there'll be a letter stamped
   In Asia. Who can tell?

—Unknown

# Taking Off

The airplane taxis down the field
And heads into the breeze,
It lifts its wheels above the ground,
It skims above the trees,
It rises high and higher
Away up toward the sun,
It's just a speck against the sky,
And now...
—And now it's gone!

—Unknown

# Popcorn

Pop, pop, popcorn,
popping in the pot,
pop, pop, popcorn,
eat it while it's hot!

Pop, pop, popcorn,
butter on the top,
when I eat popcorn,
I can't stop!

—Helen H. Moore

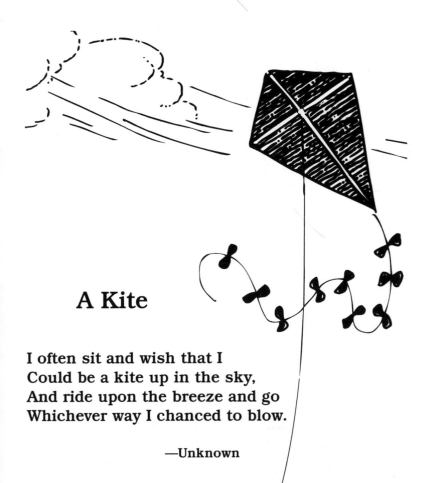

# A Kite

I often sit and wish that I
Could be a kite up in the sky,
And ride upon the breeze and go
Whichever way I chanced to blow.

—Unknown

# My Shoe

OO-oo-oo-oo-oo!
I cannot tie my shoe!
I've tried and I've tried—
But it just won't be tied—
No matter what I do!

—Helen H. Moore

# Cricket

The noisy cricket
Soaks up the moonbeams
On the wet lawn.

—Japan, 20th century

# THE FIREFLY
# LIGHTS HIS LAMP

Although the night is damp,
The little firefly ventures out,
And slowly lights his lamp.

—Unknown
(Japanese)

# Riddle #1

White sheep, white sheep, on a blue hill,
When the wind stops, you all stand still.
When the wind blows, you run away slow,
White sheep, white sheep, where do you go?

Answer: Clouds
—Unknown

# Riddle #2

I can walk on this
If it's wet or dry;
I can put it in a pail
And make a pie.
If I hold it in my hands
It will trickle through,
I can find it at the seaside
And so can you.

Answer: Sand
—Unknown

# Riddle #3

I am round like a ball
And I live in the sky,
You will see me at night
If you look up high.

**Answer: the Moon**
**—Unknown**

# Riddle #4

You can see me in the country,
You can see me in the town.
Sometimes I am up,
And sometimes I am down.
If the sun shines very brightly
I am never there at all;
But everyone can see me
When the rain begins to fall.

Answer: Umbrella
—Unknown

# Elephants at Play

One elephant went out to play
On a spider's web one day.
She had such a lot of fun,
She called for another elephant to come.

Two elephants went out to play
On a spider's web one day.
They had such a lot of fun,
They called for another elephant to come.

Three elephants went out to play,
On a spider's web one day.
The spider came along to say,
"You'll break my web! Now go away!"

—Unknown

# The Apple Tree

Way up high in the apple tree
One little apple smiled at me.
I shook that tree as hard as I could.
Down came an apple and mmmmmm!
  Was it good!

Way up high in the apple tree
Two little apples....
Mmmm... were they good

—Valerie SchifferDanoff

## In the Beehive

Here is beehive,
but where are the bees?
Hidden inside, where nobody sees.
Watch as they come out of their hive,
one, two, three, bees,
four bees, five!

—Unknown

# Runaway Ducks

Six little ducks went out one day,
Over the hill and far away.
Mother duck said,
"Quack! Quack! Quack!"
But just <u>five</u> ducks
came quacking back.

Five little ducks....

—Unknown

# Jumping Monkeys

Five little monkeys
Jumping on the bed.
One fell off
And bumped his head.
Mama called the doctor,
And the doctor said,
"That's what you get
For jumping on the bed!"

Four little monkeys...

—Unknown